Y0-BDH-478

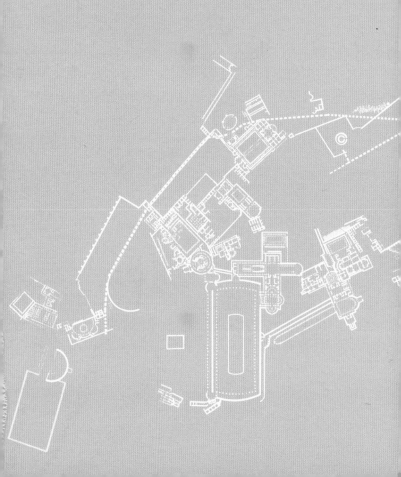

HADRIAN'S VILLA

*between heaven
and earth*

A tour with
**Marguerite
Yourcenar**

Nicoletta Lanciano

ἄπειρον
ἄπειρον
ἄπειρον
ἄπειρον
ἄπειρον
ἄπειρον
APEIRON

"What sparked the whole idea as far as I'm concerned was a visit I made when I was twenty to the villa Adriana."

With Open Eyes, p. 117

Introduction

The tour of Hadrian's Villa, with Marguerite Yourcenar's texts as guide, is the result of research based on "a direct rapport with things", as Zeno writes in *The Abyss*. Research inspired by my familiarity with Villa Adriana and motivated by a desire to get to know and care for the buildings and the open spaces that blend into a harmonious whole with the sky and with their natural surroundings.

This tour, in fact, was prompted initially by my visits to the Villa and by Marguerite Yourcenar's novel, *Memoirs of Hadrian* and, subsequently, by her other writings.

At first, the aim of my research in the Villa was to identify the location chosen as "an observatory"* for Hadrian, who since childhood had observed with deep interest "the world of the spheres".*
Therefore, while looking down at the stones and foundations of the buildings, with the intention of studying the Villa's layout, I would, at the same time, look upwards to study the sky, the position of the sun, and the surrounding horizon.
This also gave rise to a very brief exchange of letters with Marguerite Yourcenar. When I first wrote to her I intended to ask her just one question. Where did she think Hadrian's Astronomic Observatory was located within the Villa? Her reply reopened my research, because, apart from indicating any elevated place as a possible observatory, such as a wooden terrace or a roof, she mentioned a site that

* *Memoirs of Hadrian*, p. 148

One of the more original and interesting architectonic structures in Fatehpur-Sikri

raises questions similar to those relating to Villa Adriana: Fatehpur-Sikri, in India. Fatehpur-Sikri, too, is an imperial Villa/town, known for its architecture, fountains and pools built by Akbar, a learned king with an interest in the stars, who, around 1550, moved the capital from Agra, 40 km further west, to Fatehpur-Sikri.

I had also sent her a map of the sky with the constellation of Antinous. In her reply, she made a point of expressing her gratitude to me. Our correspondence ended with her death in 1987.

Some locations in the Villa have caused me to reflect on life, death, and immortality, on the Villa's relation to the city of Rome, which can be discerned on the horizon, and to the rest of the known world and its inhabitants; on the journeys

Petit Plaisance
Northeast Harbor
Maine · 04612 - US

29 juillet 86

chères ~~Claudine~~ Claudine di Monti
et Nicoletta ~~Amadore~~ Lanciano -

Merci pour la belle carte fragmentaire
du ciel. Quant à votre question, je ne saurais
comment y répondre : un observatoire, ou peut-être
simplement une haute terrasse en terrain clair, a
dû certainement exister à la ville, mais où. Il
a pu s'agir d'une terrasse au sommet de
un édifice prolongé, ou aussi d'une haute
plateforme en bois.

Des incertitudes presque aussi grandes
planent sur l'observatoire d'Akbar, à
Fatapur Sikri, en Inde, qui était probablement
le plus important des deux, vus l'immense
développement de la science astronomique et
des études astrologiques à l'époque.

Bien sympathiquement à vous,

Marguerite Yourcenar

which, as well as allowing the exploration of the Empire in every direction, also represent many stages in self-reflection and inner life so typical of the stoic tradition. Moreover, some buildings call to mind other Roman buildings connected with Hadrian, such as the Pantheon and Castel Sant'Angelo, to which I have dedicated a few passages.

Hadrian's interest in the stars, in the phenomena and objects of the sky, in the movement of celestial bodies, studied by the astronomers of the period, is testified by the Emperor's two biographers, Spartianus and Cassius Dio, from whom Marguerite Yourcenar has widely drawn. It is the theme that has inspired the choices of extracts and the stages of the tour that follows.

The proposed itinerary is, therefore, a tour that anticipates some pauses in the Villa in order to interpret the location and "to listen" to some texts.

These are not archaeological "explanations" of the different places, but rather, "evocations" prompted by their imagined purpose and by what can be seen in the Villa and its surroundings.

The names given to the various places are those handed down to us by tradition, even though researchers continue to question many of them.

I have deliberately used very few and, I hope, clear words to introduce Marguerite Yourcenar's texts relating to the various places so as not to be an obstacle to the enjoyment of the texts and the Villa's buildings; texts and buildings to which visitors can relate in their own way. My words are meant to indicate only the route and the stages at which to pause to read and to make clear the connection that I found between the place and the text.

At times I have taken the opportunity to quote extensively from the writings of those authors who have particularly influenced me in the interpretation of the sites.

Rome, April 2003
Nicoletta Lanciano

The quotations from the books by Marguerite Yourcenar refer to the following editions:

Memoirs of Hadrian, Farrar, Straus and Giroux 1990. Translation by Grace Frick.

The Dark Brain of Piranesi and Other Essays, Aidan Ellis Publishing Ltd 1985. Translation by Richard Howard.

En pèlerin et en étranger, Gallimard 1989. Translation of the quotations in this book by Amina Santcross.

With Open Eyes – Conversations with Mathieu Galey, Beacon Press 1984. Translation by Arthur Goldhammer.

Lettres à ses amis et quelques autres, Gallimard 1995, édition établie, présentée et annotée par Michèle Sarde et Joseph Brami. Translation of the quotations in this book by Amina Santcross.

Ganymede and the Eagle of Zeus, or *Apotheosis of Antinous*, mosaic from
Hadrian's Villa, now in the collection of the Vatican Museums.
On Ganymede and the Eagle and the Constellation of Antinous see also
page 50ff in this booklet.

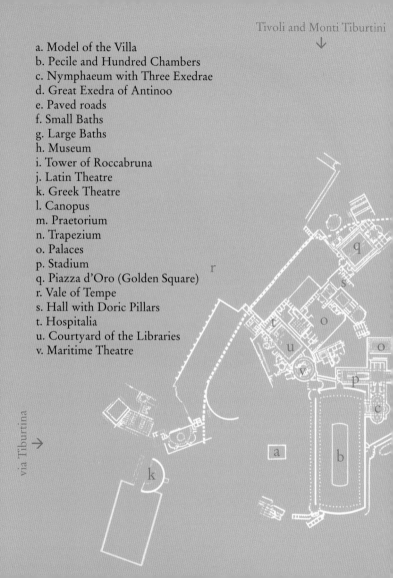

a. Model of the Villa
b. Pecile and Hundred Chambers
c. Nymphaeum with Three Exedrae
d. Great Exedra of Antinoo
e. Paved roads
f. Small Baths
g. Large Baths
h. Museum
i. Tower of Roccabruna
j. Latin Theatre
k. Greek Theatre
l. Canopus
m. Praetorium
n. Trapezium
o. Palaces
p. Stadium
q. Piazza d'Oro (Golden Square)
r. Vale of Tempe
s. Hall with Doric Pillars
t. Hospitalia
u. Courtyard of the Libraries
v. Maritime Theatre

via Tiburtina
→

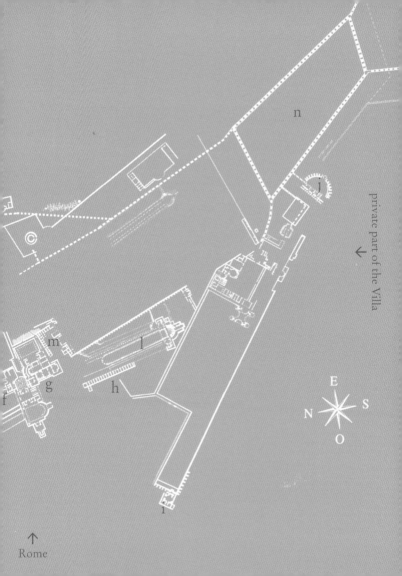

private part of the Villa

←

n

j

©

m

l

f

g

h

i

E

N ✳ S

O

Rome

The Villa is a living place – on the threshold

We are on the threshold of a suburban villa, outside the town. It is a villa, which in its urban planning is like a small town in which, however, unlike in a real town, it is not possible to distinguish clearly between the spaces as they merge into each other.

The proposed itinerary goes anti-clockwise, from west to east through the south, just like the rotation of Earth in space. It is the same direction taken by the chariots in Circuses and that athletes nowadays follow when running in a stadium. The following texts, however, can be read at the indicated sites independently from the followed itinerary.

From the entrance, along an ascending avenue, we reach a covered building in which there is a scale model of the Villa. Next, we turn towards the west, on the visitor's right, and stop near the rounded end of the wall of the Pecile.

The Villa is a living place for the presence of animals in the sky, on the land, and in the water; for the ancient and aromatic plants; for the response of the many visitors who pass through it every day and arrive here from all over the world; for the research which it inspires; for the restorations and the never interrupted archaeological excavations. The Villa is a living place despite its ruins. In autumn, I have often found tables and large sheets spread out under the trees ready for the olive harvest.

My four-year-old son on his second visit to the Villa, before we entered, asked, "Has the Emperor invited us, then?" From then on that question, which makes one smile and feel disquieted at the same time, has never stopped to amaze me – as children's questions often do. It is a question that continues to stay with me.

Once, before dawn, I was able to walk through the Villa with a guide. He showed me the aromatic, culinary, and medicinal herbs, grown in many hidden corners of the Villa. For all these reasons I think of the Villa as a living place.

We enter with one question in mind: which building had the Emperor destined for the observation of the stars? Which was his Observatory, if indeed there was one? This question, however, raises another, much more complex question. What is the relation, the dialogue, between sky and Earth, between the light of day and the sky at night, and also

between human attitudes and passions, which Marguerite Yourcenar's texts help us to understand?

Thus we proceed through the Villa with one aim, without looking in the texts that follow for a "description" or "explanation" or "an hypothesis on the purpose" of the spaces. Many other books deal with this.

It is said that Hadrian brought here his most beautiful memories from the most far-away lands. We are in the place where the memory of past journeys resides; the memory of other times, other images and other places. Hadrian built this Villa with the echo, with the evocation of his journeys, and with materials gathered from all the diverse regions of the Empire. Marbles and stones come from distant lands – from the coasts of Africa and of the Orient – very distant places in an age with different technology and means of transport, at a time when, for the Romans, the borders of the Empire were the borders of the known world.

"Yesterday, at the Villa, I thought of the thousands of lives, silent and furtive as those of wild beasts, unthinking as those of plants, who have followed in succession here between Hadrian's time and ours: gypsies of Piranesi's day, pillagers of the ruins, beggars, goatherds, and peasants lodged as best they could in some corner of the rubble. At the end of an olive grove, in an ancient corridor partly cleared, G. and I came upon a shepherd's bed of rushes, with his improvised clothes-peg stuck between two blocks of Roman cement, and the ashes of his fire not yet cold. A sense of intimacy with humble, ordinary things, a little like what one feels at the Louvre when, after closing hour, the cots of the guardians appear in among the statues."

Reflections on the Composition of Memoirs of Hadrian, p. 345

"Marullinus, my grandfather, believed in the stars
[...]
They said that he was a wizard, and the village folk tried
to avoid his glance. But over animals he had singular
powers. I have watched his grizzled head approaching cautiously, though in friendly wise, toward a nest
of adders, and before a lizard have seen his gnarled
fingers execute a kind of dance. On summer nights he
took me with him to study the sky from the top of a
barren hill. I used to fall asleep in a furrow, tired out

from counting meteors. He would stay sitting, gazing upward and turning imperceptibly with the stars. He must have known the systems of Philolaus and of Hipparchus, and that of Aristarchus of Samos which was my choice in later years, but these speculations had ceased to interest him. For him the stars were fiery points in the heavens, objects akin to the stones and slow-moving insects from which he also drew portents, constituent parts of a magic universe in which were combined the will of the gods, the influence of demons,

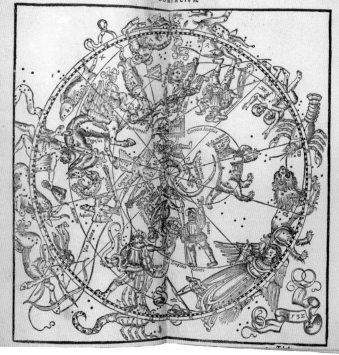

and the lot apportioned to men. He had cast my horoscope. One night (I was eleven years old at the time) he came and shook me from my sleep and announced, with the same grumbling laconism that he would have employed to predict a good harvest to his tenants, that I should rule the world. Then, seized with mistrust, he went to fetch a brand from the small fire of root ends

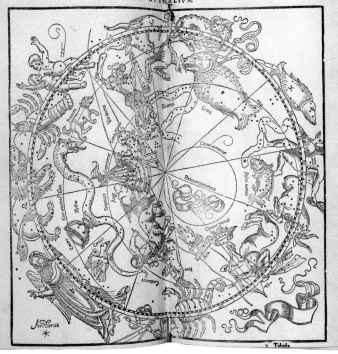

IMAGINES CONSTELLATIONVM
AVSTRALIVM.

kept going to warm us through the colder hours, held it over my hand, and read in my solid, childish palm I know not what confirmation of lines written in the sky. The world for him was all of a piece; a hand served to confirm the stars. His news affected me less than one might think; a child is ready for anything."

Memoirs of Hadrian, pp. 29-31

"From the nights of my childhood, when Marullinus first pointed out to me the constellations above, my curiosity for the world of the spheres has not abated. In the watches of camp life I looked with wonder at the moon as it raced through the clouds of barbarian skies; in later years, in the clear nights of Attica, I listened while Theron of Rhodes, the astronomer, explained his system of the world. In mid-Aegean, lying flat on the deck of a ship, I have followed the slow oscillation of the mast as it moved among the stars, swaying first from the red eye of Taurus to the tears of the Pleiades, then from Pegasus to the Swan. I answered as well as I could the naive questions so gravely put by the youth gazing with me at that same sky. **Here at the Villa I have built an observatory,** but I can no longer climb its steps. Once in my life I did a rarer thing. I made sacrifice to the constellations of an entire night. It was after my visit to Osroës, coming back through the Syrian desert: lying on my back, wide awake but abandoning for some hours every human concern, I gave myself up from nightfall to dawn to this world of crystal and flame. That was the most glorious of all my voyages. Overhead shone the great star of the constellation of Lyra, destined to be the polar star for men who will live tens of thousands of years after we have ceased to be. In the last light of the horizon Castor and Pollux gleamed faintly; the Serpent gave way to the Archer;

next the Eagle mounted toward the zenith, wings widespread, and beneath him appeared the constellation at that time unnamed by astronomers, but to which I have since given that most cherished of names. The night, which is never so black as people think who live and sleep indoors, was at first more dark, and then grew lighter. The fires, left burning to frighten the jackals, went out; their dying coals made me think of my grandfather warming himself as he stood in his vineyard, and of his prophecies, which by then had become the present, and were soon to be the past."

Memoirs of Hadrian, pp. 148-149

"The attitude I attributed to Hadrian in *Mémoires d'Hadrien* is almost similar to [that of] Zeno [who] had long before given up examining astrological themes, deeming our relationship with these far away spheres too confusing to obtain definite conclusions from them, even though here and there strange results occurred [...] We know that like all men of his time, he was interested in astrology, even if certain chroniclers seemed to have exaggerated in this respect. In fact, it is doubtful if Hadrian used to spend the first of January commenting in detail on the events of the year ahead."

Lettres à ses amis et quelques autres, July 1979, p. 606

The city of Rome

Facing the west from a high point we look at the country-side and, far away on the horizon, there where the sun sets, we discern the city of Rome.
We recall some of the thoughts of the Emperor on the history and life of the city, from which, at times, he wished to stay away.

"...the divinity of the Eternal City was now for the first time identified with the Mother of Love, inspirer of every joy. It was a basic concept in my life. The Roman power was thus taking on that cosmic and sacred character, that pacific, protective form which I aspired to give it."

Memoirs of Hadrian, p. 166

"For some years now people have credited me with strange insight, and with knowledge of divine secrets.

But they are mistaken; I have no such power. It is true, however, that during those nights of Bethar some disturbing phantoms passed before my eyes. The perspectives afforded the mind from the height of those barren hills were less majestic than these of the Janiculum, and less golden than those of Cape Sunion; they offered the reverse and the nadir. I admitted that it was indeed vain to hope for an eternity for Athens and for Rome which is accorded neither to objects nor men, and which the wisest among us deny even to the gods. These subtle and complex forms of life, these civilizations comfortably installed in their refinements of ease and of art, the very freedom of mind to seek and to judge, all this depended upon countless rare chances, upon conditions almost impossible to bring about, and none of which could be expected to endure."

Memoirs of Hadrian, p. 242

"Rome is no longer confined to Rome: henceforth she must identify herself with half the globe, or must perish. Our homes and terraced roofs of tile, turned by the setting sun to rose and gold, are no longer enclosed, as in the time of our kings, within city walls. Our true ramparts now are thousands of leagues from Rome. I have constructed a good part of these defenses myself along the edges of Germanic forest and British moor. Each time that I have looked from afar, at the bend of some sunny road, toward a Greek acropolis with its perfect city fixed to the hill like a flower to its stem, I could not but feel that the incomparable plant was limited by its very perfection, achieved on one point of space and in one segment of time. Its sole chance of expansion, as for that of a plant, was in its seed; with the pollen of its ideas Greece has fertilized the world. But Rome, less light and less shapely, sprawling to the plain at her river's edge, was moving toward vaster growth: the city has become

the State. I should have wished the State to expand still more, likening itself to the order of the universe, to the divine nature of things. Virtues which had sufficed for the small city of the Seven Hills would have to grow less rigid and more varied if they were to meet the needs of all the earth. Rome, which I was first to venture to call "eternal", would come to be more and more like the mother deities of the cults of Asia, bearer of youths and of harvests, sheltering at her breast both the lions and the hives of bees.

But anything made by man which aspires to eternity must adapt itself to the changing rhythm of nature's great bodies, to accord with celestial time. Our Rome is no longer the village of the days of Evander, big with a future which has already partly passed by; the plundering Rome of the time of the Republic has performed its role; the mad capital of the first Caesars inclines now to greater sobriety; **other Romes will come, whose**

31

forms I see but dimly, but whom I shall have helped to mold. When I was visiting ancient cities, sacred but wholly dead, and without present value for the human race, I promised myself to save this Rome of mine from the petrification of a Thebes, a Babylon, or a Tyre. She would no longer be bound by her body of stone, but would compose for herself from the words *State*, *citizenry*, and *republic* a surer immortality. In the countries as yet untouched by our culture, on the banks of the Rhine and the Danube, or the shores of the Batavian Sea, each village enclosed within its wooden palisade brought to mind the reed hut and dunghill where our Roman twins had slept content, fed by the milk of the wolf; these cities-to-be would follow the pattern of Rome. Over separate nations and races, with their accidents of geography and history and the disparate demands of their ancestors or their gods, we should have superposed for ever a unity of human conduct and the empiricism of sober experience, but should have done so without destruction of what had preceded us. Rome would be perpetuating herself in the least of the towns where magistrates strive to demand just weight from the merchants, to clean and light the streets, to combat disorder, slackness, superstition and injustice, and to give broader and fairer interpretation to the laws. She would endure to the end of the last city built by man."

Memoirs of Hadrian, pp. 109-111

The Pecile and the chariot races

The name "Pecile" recalls the painted portico of the Agora in Athens. It consists of a wide rectangular area bordered to the north by a long wall of about 200 metres, facing east-west, the position of which allowed people to walk along it in the shade or in the sun, according to the season or their wishes. This building, thanks to its location, helps us to understand the plan of the entire Villa.

At the centre of the open space, parallel to the wall, there is a pool called "Euripus". The Euripus takes its name from a narrow strait between Euboea and Boeotia, "the transparent sea".

Around the pool there was probably a hippodrome for chariot races: it was therefore a Circus. The chariot races in the Circus had a symbolic meaning strongly associated with the sky and the stars.

We pause midway along the southern end of the pool, where is signposted, by a semicircular construction above the Hundred Chambers, the position of the seat of honour, from which it was possible to watch the races without ever having the sun shining in one's eyes.

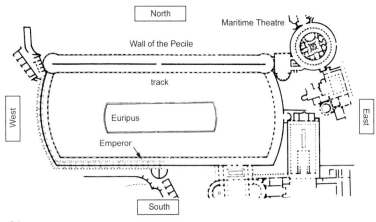

The triumph of the Sun and the Moon with the signs of Leo and Cancer

"And it is here that I can best speak of **a habit which led me throughout my life along paths less secret than those of Eleusis, but after all parallel to them, namely, the study of the stars**. I have always been friend to astronomers and client to astrologers. The science of the latter is questionable, but if false in its details it is perhaps true in the total implication; for if man is part and parcel of the universe, and is ruled by the same laws as govern the sky, it is not unreasonable to search the heavens for the patterns of our lives, and for those impersonal attractions which induce our successes and our errors. On autumn evenings I seldom failed to greet Aquarius to the south, that heavenly Cup Bearer and Giver of Gifts under whose sign I was born. Nor did I forget to note in each of their passages Jupiter and Venus, who govern my life, nor to measure the dangerous influence of Saturn.

But if this strange refraction of human affairs upon the stellar vault preoccupied many of my waking hours, I was still more deeply absorbed in celestial mathematics, the abstract speculations to which those flaming spheres give rise. I was inclined to believe, along with certain of our more daring philosophers, that earth, too, takes part in that daily and nightly round which the sacred processions of Eleusis are intended to reproduce in human terms. In a world which is only a vortex of forces and whirl of atoms, where there is neither high nor low, periphery nor center, I could ill conceive of a globe without motion, or a fixed point which would not move.

[...]

Both the man and the stars which are the objects of his gaze roll inevitably toward their ends, marked somewhere in the sky; but each moment of that descent is a pause, a guide mark, and a segment of a curve itself as solid as a chain of gold. Each movement in space brings us back to a point which, because we happen to be on it, seems to us a center."

Memoirs of Hadrian, pp. 146-148

"The circus mirrors the sky. We owe it to the wise Ancients that the shape of the circus reflects the shape of the sky and the number of its heavenly borders. In fact, the twelve openings of the stalls represent the twelve months and the twelve constellations crossed by the golden-rayed stars as they travel through the sky. The four horses recall the seasons and the four colours of the factions represent the elements. The charioteer, like Phoebus, harnesses the four horses. The gates enclose, each within their own space, the quadrigae, to which Janus gives the starting signal by raising a flag. Then, when the barriers open and the chariots burst forth, everyone thinks only of overpowering the others and all strive to complete the circuit defined by the start and finish lines. These two symmetrical points indicate the rising and setting of the Sun. Between these two points, stretches the Euripus which recalls the vast area covered by the seas, and in the middle, towering above all else, the obelisk marks the centre. Furthermore, it takes seven days, corresponding to the seven concentric circles that delimit the boundaries of the sky, to complete the course and attain the palm branch of victory. The biga is always dedicated to the Moon, the quadriga to the Sun, and only the horses are ritually dedicated to Castor and his brother. Our spectacles are in harmony with the divine world, and their powerful fascination has been enhanced by the homage paid to the gods."

Anthologie latine edited by J. Beaujeu, quoted in H. Stierlin, *op.cit.*, p. 138

In some Hebrew texts there are descriptions of Solomon's throne and his Hippodrome, which recalls the passion of the Judean King for his horses:

"A chariot had two men. The two men carried the harness which they then placed on the four horses for the race in

The magistrate starts the chariot race

39

the hippodrome, which had been ordered by the king. […] How many races did the king organise in the hippodrome each year? There were twelve stewards altogether and for everything, and each steward was in charge of the race of the month. […] And what was the length of the hippodrome? Three parasangs by three, and a track one parasang wide (the parasang is a Persian measure corresponding to 5/6 km.). In the centre there were some posts and some cages and all kinds of wild beasts and fowls that had been placed therein. And around them raced the horses. They raced eight times a day. And on which day did they race in the hippodrome? On the first day of the month. For on the second day, at that time, the king attended to all those who came to the city from the countryside and from all nations of the world. On the third day of the month he devoted himself to the magic arts. Where did he have his consultations? In front of the Temple, that is in the Garden of Eden. […] The king's hippodrome consisted of four sections and each section contained 41.000 men. The four sections were distinguished by four colours: sky blue for the king, his servants, the sages, the priests and the Levites; white for the Hebrews; red for all those who came from the city and from the countryside; green for the nations of the world, come from afar bearing gifts for the king. And why this attire? Because of the four seasons."

Henri Stierlin, *L'astrologia e il potere*,
pp. 159-160 (*Astrology and Power*)

Every palace and every town has its own Circus. In Rome there are many, but the largest is the Palatine Circus: the Circo Massimo. Other famous circuses are those of Villa Armerina in Sicily (4th century B.C.), of Antioch, of Thessalonica, of Trier, and of Constantinople.

In the centre of a Circus there is an Euripus filled with water, or a spina decorated with obelisks, statues, and columns, as can be seen in many bas-reliefs and mosaics.

To the Nymphæum with three Exedrae
– architecture and town planning

We continue on the southern side of the exterior border of
the Pecile and enter the Nymphæum with three Exedrae.

The Nymphæum with three Exedrae in front of the Palace,
on the west side, has many columns with beautiful pedestals
and ornate capitals. We pause near a niche where, resting on
the ground, there are some that depict the shapes of animals
and plants.
Hadrian left tangible signs on earth through his architecture
and town planning.

"**To build is to collaborate with earth,** to put a human
mark upon a landscape, modifying it forever thereby;
the process also contributes to that slow change which
makes up the history of cities. What thought and care

to determine the exact site for a bridge, or for a fountain, and to give a mountain road that perfect curve which is at the same time the shortest. [...]

I have done much rebuilding. To reconstruct is to collaborate with time gone by, penetrating or modifying its spirit, and carrying it toward a longer future. Thus beneath the stones we find the secret of the springs.

Our life is brief: we are always referring to centuries which precede or follow our own as if they were totally alien to us, but I have come close to them in my play with stone. These walls which I reinforce are still warm from contact with vanished bodies; hands yet unborn will caress the shafts of these columns. The more I have meditated upon my death, and especially upon that of another, the more I have tried to add to our lives these virtually indestructible extensions. At Rome I preferred to use our enduring brick; it returns

but slowly to the earth, from which it comes, and its imperceptible settling and crumbling leave a mountainous mass even when the edifice has ceased to be visibly what it was built for, a fortress, a circus, or a tomb. In Greece and in Asia I chose the native marble, that fair substance which, once cut, stays so faithful to human measurements and proportions that the plan of an entire temple survives in each fragment of a broken column.

Architecture is rich in possibilities more varied than Vitruvius' four orders would seem to allow; our great stone blocks, like our tones in music, are amenable to endless regrouping. For the Pantheon I turned to the ancient Etruria of augurs and soothsayers; the sunny temple of Venus, on the contrary, is a round of Ionic forms, a profusion of white and pale rose columns clustered about the voluptuous goddess whence sprang the race of Caesar. The Olympieion of Athens, built on the plain, had to be in exact counterpoise to the Parthenon on its hill, vastness opposed to perfection, ardor kneeling before calm, splendor at the feet of beauty. The chapels of Antinous and his temples were magic chambers, commemorating a mysterious passage between life and death; these shrines to an overpowering joy and grief were places of prayer and evocation of the dead. [...]

Plotinopolis, Hadrianopolis, Antinoöpolis, Hadrianotherae... I have multiplied these human beehives as much as possible. Plumber and mason, engineer and

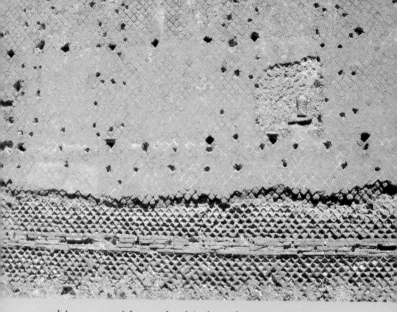

architect preside at the births of cities; the operation also requires certain magical gifts. In a world still largely made up of woods, desert, and uncultivated plain, a city is indeed a fine sight, with its paved streets, its temple to some god or other, its public baths and toilets, a shop where the barber discusses with his clients the news from Rome, its pastry shop, shoestore, and perhaps a bookshop, its doctor's sign, and a theatre, where from time to time a comedy of Terence is played. Our men of fashion complain of the uniformity of our cities; they suffer in seeing everywhere the same statue of the emperor, and the same water pipes.

They are wrong: the beauty of Nîmes is wholly different from that of Arles. But that very uniformity, to be found now on three continents, reassures the traveler as does the sight of a milestone: even the dullest of our towns have their comforting significance as shelters and posting stops. A city: that framework constructed by men for men, monotonous if you will, but only as are wax cells laden with honey, a place of meeting and exchange, where peasants come to sell their produce, and linger to gape and stare at the paintings of a portico...

My cities were born of encounters, both my own encounters with given corners of the earth and the conjunction of my plans as emperor with the incidents of my personal life. Plotinopolis grew from the need to establish new market towns in Thrace, but also from the tender desire to honor Plotina. Hadrianotherae is designed to serve as a trading town for the forest dwellers of Asia Minor: at first it had been for me a summer retreat, with its forest full of wild game, its hunting lodge of rough hewn logs below the hill of the god Attys, and its headlong stream where we bathed each morning. Hadrianopolis in Epirus reopened an urban center in the heart of an impoverished province: it owes its start to a visit which I made to the oracle of Dodona. Hadrianopolis in Thrace, an agricultural and military outpost strategically placed on the edge of barbarian lands, is populated by veterans of the Sarmatian wars: I know at first hand the strength and the weakness of each one of those men, their names, the number of their years of service, and of their wounds. Antinoöpolis, dearest of all, born on the site of sorrow, is confined to a narrow band of arid soil between the river and the cliffs. I was only the more desirous, therefore, to enrich it with other resources, trade with India, river traffic, and the learned graces of a Greek metropolis. There is not a place on earth that I care less to revisit, but there are few to which I have devoted more pains. It is a veritable city of columns, a perpetual peristyle. I exchange dispatches with its governor, Fidus Aquila, about the propylaea of its temple and the statues of its triumphal arch; I have

chosen the names of its district divisions and religious and administrative units, symbolic names both obvious and secret which catalogue all my memories. I myself drew the plan of its Corinthian colonnades and the corresponding alignment of palm trees spaced regularly along the river banks. Countless times have I walked in thought that almost perfect quadrilateral, cut by parallel streets and divided in two by the broad avenue which leads from a Greek theatre to a tomb."

Memoirs of Hadrian, pp. 126-130

In front of the Great Exedra of Antinous

From above the Hundred Chambers we overlook an open space where excavations have brought to light the paved roads which, on the north-west side, gave access to the Villa, passing below the Hundred Chambers and the retaining wall, towards the Vestibule.

Beyond the streets can be seen the foundations of the Great Exedra, in which have been discovered many fragments of sculptures in the Egyptian style, among which, the statues of Antinous-Osiris. These archaeological finds call to mind Egypt, the land where Antinous, the young boy from

Bithynia, Hadrian's favourite, drowned in the Nile.

Many different portrayals of this young boy have been found throughout the Empire, on bas-reliefs, statues, mosaics and on coins.

However, since the astronomers at the time of Hadrian named part of the sky Antinous, either because the Emperor wished it, or because they wanted to pay homage to him, globes and astronomic maps also show portrayals of this young man.

Moreover, Hadrian's interest in the sky and his visits to the Library of Alexandria demonstrate the Emperor's links with places where, at that time, astronomy was being studied. It is not surprising, therefore, that in the Almagest, the astronomical manual compiled by Ptolemy of Alexandria

ἀστέρες θ, ὧν β′ μεγέθους ᾱ, γ′ δ, δ′ ᾱ, ε′ γ.

Οἱ περὶ τὸν Ἀετόν, ἐφ' ὧν ὁ Ἀντίνοος.

τῶν ἀπὸ νότου τῆς κεφαλῆς τοῦ Ἀετοῦ β ὁ προηγούμενος

in 137 A.D., the constellation of Antinous is situated near the constellations of the Eagle and of Aquarius. The Eagle, moreover, represents Ganymede, Jupiter's favourite, and the constellation of Aquarius is the one under which Hadrian himself was born.

Indeed Ovid writes:
"The king of the gods once burned with love for Phrygian Ganymede, and to win him Jupiter chose to be something other than he was. Yet he did not deign to transform himself into any other bird, than that eagle, that could carry his

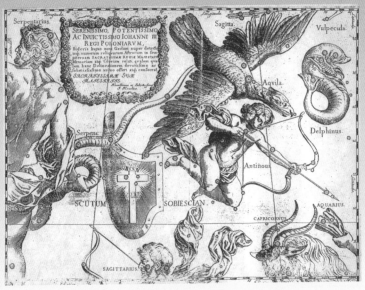

Star Atlas with the constellation of Antinous

lightning bolts. Straightaway, he beat the air with deceitful wings, and stole the Trojan boy, who still handles the mixing cups, and against Juno's will pours out Jove's nectar."

Ovid, *The Metamorphoses*, Book X, translation A.S. Kline

The constellation of Antinous, however, has disappeared from astronomic manuals, with the revision of the boundaries of the constellations in 1922. After 1800 years the stars that belonged to this asterism are now part of the nearby constellations. This decision was probably taken also for ethical motives. Indeed F. Boquet, in his *Storia dell'Astronomia*, writes in 1922, "If during Hadrian's reign it was dared to honour in such a way his graceful Antinous, and if this constellation so ignobly named, has remained in the celestial iconography until now, the Moderns [in capital letters in the text, (ed.)] have had the good taste to omit its name from it."

"This evening, returning from a visit to the camp at Auschwitz, where the flesh and soul of human kind endured so many indescribable torments before being reduced to mere ash, I happened to receive your poems. [...] Personally, I have never understood why so many readers of the *Mémoires* are interested only in the **Antinous episode**, instead of seeing this event as I do, as only a part (moving, I admit) of the life of an Emperor who knew how to be a good administrator of the world, a man of action on whom the best of ancient civilisation had left its mark. By thus separating sensual pleasure from the remaining emotions and human experiences, I believe we debase it and in so doing reject the confusing totality of our heritage as human beings."

Lettres à ses amis et quelques autres, Krakow, April 1964, p. 200

"One evening Chabrias [Orphic initiate (ed.)] called me to show me a star, till then hardly visible, in the constellation of the Eagle; it flashed like a gem and pulsated like a heart. **I chose it for his star** [of Antinous (ed.)] and his sign. Each night I would follow its course until utterly

Constellation of Antinous. Floor of the sundial (detail),
Naples, Museo di S. Martino

wearied; in that part of the sky I have seen strange
radiance. Folk thought me mad, but that was of little
consequence."

Memoirs of Hadrian, p. 205

"... the Eagle mounted toward the zenith, wings widespread, and beneath him appeared the constellation
at that time unnamed by astronomers, but to which I
have since given that most cherished of names."

Memoirs of Hadrian, p. 148

"They would have had me see the resplendent god [...] I had created that god; I believed in him, in my way, but a brilliant posthumous destiny in the midst of the stellar spheres failed to compensate for so brief a life; the god did not take the place of the living being I had lost.

I was incensed by man's mania for clinging to hypotheses while ignoring facts, for mistaking his dreams for more than dreams."

Memoirs of Hadrian, p. 208

"Like a man uncertain of his next stop who reserves lodgings in several hostelries at a time, I ordered a monument for him [Antinous (ed.)] at Rome, on the banks of the Tiber near my own tomb, but thought also of the Egyptian chapels which I had had built at the Villa by caprice, and which were suddenly proving tragically useful."

Memoirs of Hadrian, p. 199

"An obelisk nine metres high, with an inscription in hieroglyphic writing, paid homage to the Egyptian Antinous, the true one, the personified son of Beauty. He is also shown offering sacrifice to the god Amon-Re." It is, as Gregorovius points out, the Obelisk that now stands on the Pincian Hill where it was placed in 1822. This is the only obelisk showing the transcription of the name of Rome in hieroglyphic script.

"*G:* All the same, contemporaries must have been quite surprised by the cult of Antinous and by the innumerable effigies of him that Hadrian had strewn about the empire. Yet there was apparently no resistance –

Y: There was most likely some passive resistance from the old-Roman camp, as the fact that there are no Roman coins of Antinous suggests. Decisions concerning the striking of coinage in Rome were the privilege of the Senate. Coins depicting Antinous are known from almost everywhere, from Asia Minor as well as all the Greek cities. But there is no Roman coin, even though Hadrian would certainly have wanted one. Apparently, however, authorization was never granted, supposing the Senate was even consulted in the matter. Admittedly, the evidence is of a negative kind, but bear in mind the long-standing mutual hostility between the Senate and Hadrian, which might have led the Senate to undo all of his work had he not so skillfully arranged his own succession."

With Open Eyes, p. 126

The Baths, the Heliocaminus and the Pantheon: the cupolas with a central opening to the sky

Beyond the Pecile, towards the south, we find the Large Baths. The high vault of the Large Baths, on the avenue leading to the Canopus, with its age-old lime trees, recalls other buildings with high cupolas through which the sunlight filters: the Heliocaminus's cupola here in the Villa, near the Maritime Theatre, but above all, the much more famous and well preserved cupola of the Pantheon in Rome.

Moreover, the diameter of the round interior of the Pantheon, which is equal to the diameter of its cupola and to the height of the building – the whole equal to 150 Roman feet – appears to be equal to the diameter of the Maritime Theatre.

The Pantheon

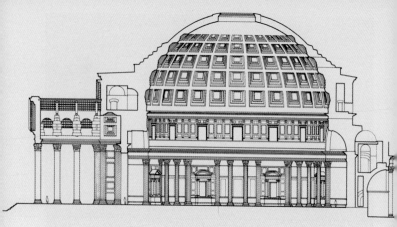

"More and more the different gods seemed to me merged mysteriously in one Whole, emanations infinitely varied, but all equally manifesting the same force; their contradictions were only expressions of an underlying accord. The construction of a temple of All Gods, a Pantheon, seemed increasingly desirable to me. I had chosen a site on the ruins of the old public baths given by Agrippa, Augustus' son-in-law, to the people of Rome. Nothing remained of the former structure except a porch and a marble plaque bearing his dedication to the Roman citizens; this inscription was carefully replaced, just as before, on the front of the new temple. It mattered little to me to have my name recorded on this monument, which was the product of my very thought. On the contrary, it pleased me that a text of more than a century ago should link this new edifice to the beginning of our empire, to that reign

which Augustus had brought to peaceful conclusion. Even in my innovations I liked to feel that I was, above all, a continuator."

Memoirs of Hadrian, p. 166-167

"The date chosen for this festival was the anniversary of Rome's birth, the eighth day following the Ides of April in the eight hundred and eighty-second year after the founding of the City. [...]
On the same day, with graver solemnity, as if muted, a dedicatory ceremony took place inside the **Pantheon**. I myself had revised the architectural plans, drawn with too little daring by Apollodorus: utilizing the arts of Greece only as ornamentation, like an added luxury, I had gone back for the basic form of the structure to primitive, fabled times of Rome, to the round temples of ancient Etruria. My intention had been

that this sanctuary of All Gods should reproduce the likeness of the terrestrial globe and of the stellar sphere, that globe wherein are enclosed the seeds of eternal fire, and that hollow sphere containing all. Such was also the form of our ancestors' huts where the smoke of man's earliest hearths escaped through an orifice at the top. The cupola, constructed of a hard but light-weight volcanic stone which seemed still to share in the upward movement of names, revealed the sky through a great hole at the center, showing alternately dark and blue. This temple, both open and mysteriously enclosed, was conceived as a solar quadrant. The hours would make their round on that caissoned ceiling, so carefully polished by Greek artisans; the disk of daylight would rest suspended there like a shield of gold; rain would form its clear pool on the pavement below; prayers would rise like smoke toward that void where we place the gods."

Memoirs of Hadrian, p. 168

"In the worst hours of apathy and dejection I would go for solace to Hartford's fine museum, seeking out a Canaletto painting of Rome, the Pantheon standing brown and gold against the blue sky of a late afternoon in summer; and each time I would come away from it comforted, and once again at peace."

Reflections on the Composition of Memoirs of Hadrian, p. 323

To the Museum

To the west of the Canopus there is a small museum. We stop at the entrance in front of "the beautiful olive tree", a majestic plant that is 1200 years old.

"The Hellenized and neoclassical art of Hadrian's time, the official and rather heavy art of Marcus Aurelius's abound in the biographers' sense of these two wise emperors; the obelisk on the Pincio corroborates in hieroglyphics Spartianus's account of the death of Antinous in Egypt; the stuccos of the Pythagorean basilica at Porta Maggiore attest to the poetic pagan piety which continued to inspire idealistic souls between Hadrian and Alexander Severus, as it is evoked, for instance, by Lampridius's description of the latter's private chapel. The civilized graces of Hadrian's villa, to which Aurelian later relegated his captive Zenobia, the enormous ruins of the Septizonium in which the already orientalized court of the Severi gathered, Gallienus's pavilion near the Via Labicana, meager ves-

tiges of those imperial pleasure houses in parks planted with rare flowering plants, populated by tame beasts, which occupied a fifth of the superficies of Rome, substantiate the drama by the melancholy survival of its decor. The politics of prestige at all costs and of pleasure at any, the mindless luxury of the games and the megalomaniac processions are confirmed by the gigantic carcasses of the monuments consecrated to public diversions and comforts, the Baths of Caracalla or Diocletian, whose dimensions seem to grow and whose ornamentation to proliferate by very reason of the Empire's economic chaos, and doubtless served to kept it hidden. The puffy and microcephalic athletes of the Baths of Caracalla mosaics are indeed brothers to those gymnasts hired to strangle Commodus and sought out by Heliogabalus for other purposes. The horrible catalogues of the thousands of African and Asian wild animals subjected to the terrors and miseries of a long sea voyage and ultimately massacred to afford the comfortably seated spectators an exciting afternoon – all this waste of the substance of the world is matched not only in the Coliseum but in the provincial arenas of Italy and Spain, of Africa and Gaul; the frenzy for professional sport is still attested to by the vestiges of the Circus Maximus. But of all the constructions of the period, the Aurelian Walls indicate most tragically this mortal disease of Rome, whose temporary recoveries and inevitable relapses fill the

Historia Augusta. These majestic walls, which are still for us the very emblem of the grandeur that was Rome, were the headlong product of the years of insicurity. Each of their vaults and guard towers proclaims that the old, open Rome, sure of itself and well defended on its frontiers, has ceased to exist; immediately useful and ultimately futile, like all defensive measures, they herald the sack by Alaric a little over a hundred years away.

[...] they express the pangs of a dying economy [...]

[...] that great event whose approaching shadow nonetheless darkens the whole of the *Historia Augusta*: the death of Rome."

The Dark Brain of Piranesi and Other Essays,
"Faces of History in the *Historia Augusta*", pp. 14-16

The *Historia Augusta*, written by at least five successive authors, is the history of the Roman Emperors from Hadrian (beginning of 2nd C.) to Carinus (end of 3rd C.)

Among the olive trees

"Long ago, at the time when Greece was an India crowded but not overwhelmed by gods, a team of priests used to busy themselves here rubbing oil into the huge statue of Zeus holding Victory in his hand. We can only admire on hearsay now, this gold and ivory god, the mere mention of which reminds us that Olympus was once a place where one came to pray as well as to receive laurels of victory. But before the introduction of the cult of Zeus, other statues presided here, statues of women, like Hera, with her bovine eyes, eternal as the grass, peaceful as the creatures of the fields. The later Zeus is just a bearded double of this great sacred female [...] we are in the lap of a divine woman. The **shadowy pines** are her hair to which the **olive trees** add a few grey strands; streams and rivers are her veins; the whirlwind of victories is a mere flight of doves, whose white down is dispersed by the centuries. No doubt the muscular athletes were young trees; the supplicants, trunks, holding their two branches skywards. Everything here speaks not so much of metamorphosis as of a profound identity. **The few columns still rooted in this soil** seem surprised not to have grown branches or born flowers like the nymphs who became shrubs, like the boys who became **narcissi or hyacinths**."

En pèlerin et en étranger, pp. 11-12

To the Tower of Roccabruna

The tower given the name of Roccabruna, an elevated place facing Rome, was perhaps part of a network of towers used to exchange announcements and messages between Hadrian's Villa and the city of Rome. It is probable that, by means of light signals, coded messages were sent from tower to tower as described by Polybius in his *Histories*.

From the top of the tower the visitor can look all around, following the boundaries of the wide horizon in all directions.

"[...] Wisdom also requires changing perspectives: every new friendship gives us a fresh view of the world, as do the things we experience and the trips we take. Some methods of mental discipline recommend listening to silence, or rather, to silences, since there are dozens of different kinds. Others advise staring at the night. One oriental technique recommends bending over and looking at the landscape between one's legs. That way you see it from a different angle.

G: It would look to be upside down.

Y: Only from your point of view. There are still other variations on the theme: lie down beneath a tree and look at the sky through its leaves – yet another way of shaping the universe.

G: Such contemplative disciplines are somewhat out of keeping with your taste for travel. You once wrote somewhere that it was necessary to 'taste of the world's roundness.'

Y: It's becoming increasingly difficult to follow you. One travels in order to contemplate. Every trip is contemplation in motion. But the phrase you quote, which is uttered by the young Henry Maximilian in *The Abyss*, echoes in a rather gayer key the young

Zeno's question, 'Who would be so besotted as to die without having made at least the round of this, his prison?' I've toured my prison as extensively as I could, but there are many countries I've never visited, for various reasons: I never went to Iran, for example, because the friend who invited me died before I had a chance to go. Many planned trips had to be cancelled at the last minute. I've always had a special liking for the frontier, for gateways to realms still more wild, like the Lapland region of Sweden and Norway, parts of the Middle East where the only roads are narrow mountain trails, and the now-threatened Alaskan wilderness.

When I have Hadrian speak of his love for the barbarian countries, his predilections echo my own at times.

Throughout my life I've found the prospect of travel very alluring. When, in recent years, various circumstances conspired to keep me here all but immobilized, I at first felt a distressing sense of constraint. I told myself that I was no doubt exaggerating the value of travel in a world that has become more and more homogeneous. I have also come to appreciate the benefits of standing still. To stay in one place and watch the seasons come and go is tantamount to constant travel: one is traveling with the earth.

In short, I learned to live with 'immobility', much as Zeno did in the half of *The Abyss* (part 2) devoted to that theme. Oddly enough, immobility is described more than once in my works; indeed, I described it before I had experienced it myself, and it turned out almost exactly as I had described, except of course that the external circumstances were quite different. Yet the need to travel remained almost as powerful as carnal desire, so that lately I've 'hit the road' again and will probably do so many more times in the future, until my strength is gone.

G: You're by temperament rather adventurous.

Y: I keep moving forward, that's all. But any trip, any adventure (in the true sense of the word, which is 'that which arrives'), goes hand in hand with inner exploration. What we do and what we think bear the same relation to each other as the outer and inner curves of a vase: each models the other.

G: Would you criticize your contemporaries for being too stay-at-home?

Y: They crowd the highways, but what do they see along the way? In any case, I am suspicious of French people who say that France is enough for them and of Americans who say that you're only comfortable when you stay at home. That breed is dying out, fortunately, and is being replaced by another which does visit far-off places but only to give them a quick once-over. Like anything else, traveling requires contradictory qualities: enthusiasm, sustained attentiveness, and a certain lightheartedness, for as Baudelaire says,

> Real travelers are those who go for the sake of going,
> And who travel light, like balloons.

It also requires an ability to take pleasure in the outer spectacle of things combined with a definite willingness to go beyond that spectacle in order to discover the often hidden realities underneath. Every traveler is Ulysses and ought to be Proteus as well."

With Open Eyes, pp. 255-257

"Hadrian wasn't flashy. That's one of the things I like about him. He was above all clear-headed and always

open-minded about worlds different from his own, such as the barbarian civilizations, which may not have been so barbarous as we imagine. Making fun of Hadrian, Florus, a minor Latin poet, said: 'The emperor loves to go walking in cold climates, in the snows of Scythia and the rains of Brittany.' Hadrian's answer is roughly as follows: 'Stay in Rome, then, and go to taverns and get yourself bitten by mosquitoes while talking literature.' This feeling for the barbarian world and passionate taste for things Greek are new, though it should not be forgotten that love of Greece was typical of the best Romans in earlier times; in this respect Hadrian was merely reviving the tradition of the Scipios. Also new was the taste for the oriental world as well as the surge of religious fervor, which, though Hadrian was not its source, was contemporary with him."

With Open Eyes, p. 125

We leave Roccabruna, heading towards the Museum and follow, on the right, the path between the olive trees above the basin of the Canopus. Next we head southwards, to the private part of the Villa at present closed to the public.

The Latin Theatre and the Greek Theatre

In the privately owned area are situated the Accademia and the remains of the Theatre called Latin, while the remains of the Theatre called Greek are to be found to the north of the Villa, towards the present day entrance.

The two theatres, therefore, mark the Villa's north and south limits.

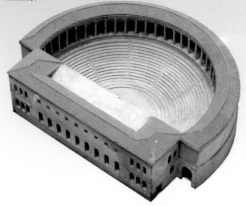

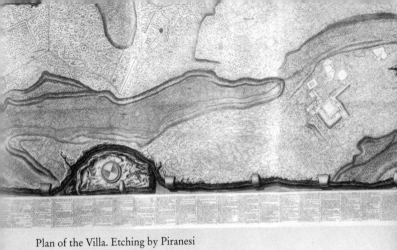

Plan of the Villa. Etching by Piranesi

"Neither the small Greek theater of the Villa, nor the Latin theater, hardly larger, had been completed, but I had a few plays produced in them nevertheless, tragedies, pantomimes, musical dramas, and old local farces. I delighted above all in the subtle gymnastics of the dance, and discovered a weakness for women with castanets, who reminded me of the region of Gades and the first spectacles which I had attended as a child. I liked that brittle sound, those uplifted arms, the furling and unfurling of veils, the dancer who changed now from woman to cloud, and then to bird, who became sometimes the ship and sometimes the wave."

Memoirs of Hadrian, p. 228-229

Behind the Serapeum of the Canopus can be seen a section of the aqueduct by means of which water could reach Villa Adriana. Indeed, the Villa needed much water for its basins, the Baths, and the needs of daily life of the many people who lived there.

To the Canopus

The "Canopus" refers to the Canopus canal, derived from an arm of the Nile between Alexandria and Abukir, and in which a port of notable commercial importance had developed. The temple built there and dedicated to Serapis became famous – writes Strabo – for its miraculous cures. Around the pool, to the north of the Serapeum, there are Roman copies and recent reproductions of statues whose originals are dispersed in museums all over the world.

"We are crowded with statues and cloyed with the exquisite in painting and sculpture, but this abundance is an illusion, for we reproduce over and over some dozen masterpieces which are now beyond our power to invent. Like other collectors I have had copied for the Villa the Hermaphrodite and the Centaur, the Niobid and the Venus. I have wanted to live as much as possible in the midst of this music of forms. I have

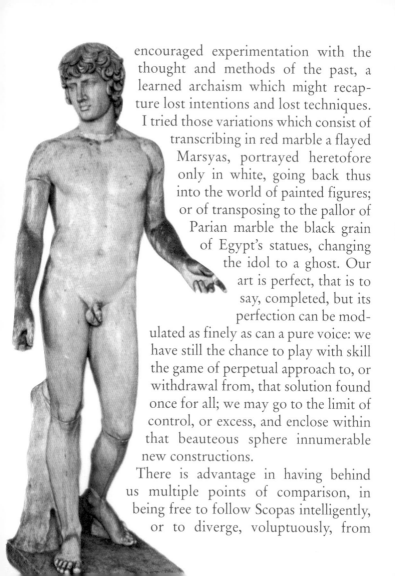

encouraged experimentation with the thought and methods of the past, a learned archaism which might recapture lost intentions and lost techniques. I tried those variations which consist of transcribing in red marble a flayed Marsyas, portrayed heretofore only in white, going back thus into the world of painted figures; or of transposing to the pallor of Parian marble the black grain of Egypt's statues, changing the idol to a ghost. Our art is perfect, that is to say, completed, but its perfection can be modulated as finely as can a pure voice: we have still the chance to play with skill the game of perpetual approach to, or withdrawal from, that solution found once for all; we may go to the limit of control, or excess, and enclose within that beauteous sphere innumerable new constructions.

There is advantage in having behind us multiple points of comparison, in being free to follow Scopas intelligently, or to diverge, voluptuously, from

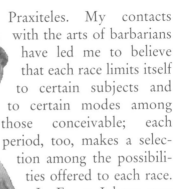

Praxiteles. My contacts with the arts of barbarians have led me to believe that each race limits itself to certain subjects and to certain modes among those conceivable; each period, too, makes a selection among the possibilities offered to each race. In Egypt I have seen colossal gods, and kings; on the wrists of Sarmatian prisoners I have found bracelets which endlessly repeat the same galloping horse, or the same serpents devouring each other. **But our art** (I mean that of the Greeks) **has chosen man as its center**. We alone have known how to show latent strength and agility in bodies in repose; we alone have made a smooth brow the symbol of wise reflection. I am like our sculptors: the human contents me; I find everything there, even what is eternal. The image of the Centaur sums up for me all forests, so greatly loved, and storm winds never breathe better than in a sea goddess' billowing scarf.

Natural objects and sacred emblems have value for me only as they are weighted with human associations: the phallic and funeral pine cone, the vase with doves which suggests siesta beside a fountain, the griffon which carries the beloved to the sky.

The art of portraiture was of slight interest to me. Our Roman busts have value only as records, faces copied to the last wrinkle, with every single wart; stencils of figures with whom we brush elbows in life, and whom we forget as soon as they die. The Greeks, on the contrary, have loved human perfection to the point of caring but little for the varied visages of men. I tend merely to glance at my own likeness, that dark face so changed by the whiteness of marble, those wide-opened eyes, that thin though sensuous mouth, controlled to the point of quivering."

Memoirs of Hadrian, pp. 130-132

We cross the area between the Prætorium and the Large Baths and make for the upper level, to the olive grove that leads to the Palace known as the Winter Palace.

The Cryptoporticus

The Villa's Cryptoporticus consists of a network of tunnels which, writes Aurigemma, permit one to go from one level to another; to take a walk when it rains or when it is too hot; to carry merchandise and tools as well as to undertake humble tasks. Many of the tunnels, in parts so wide that even horses and carts could pass through them, had vault-like roofs that were lit up either by oculi from above or from large side windows.

On the vaults and walls of the Cryptoporticus sited under the Fishpool of the Palace we find drawings, inscriptions, and names that help us to follow the story of the visitors to the Villa over the past centuries. Among the many names there is that of Piranesi, a frequent visitor, who made many engravings of this site.

"It is a Frenchman, one Jacques-Guillaume Legrand, whom we may thank for gathering from Francesco Piranesi's lips most of our details as to his father's life, views, and character; what remains of the artist's writings confirms his observations. We see a man of passionate feelings, intoxicated by work, careless of his health and his comfort, disdaining the malaria of the Roman Campagna, sustaining himself on nothing but cold rice during his long sojourns in such solitary and unhealthy sites as, at the time, Hadrian's Villa or the ruins of Albano and Cora, and lighting his scanty campfire only once a week in order to waste none of the time reserved for his explorations and his works. 'The verisimilitude and the vigor of his effects,' notes Jacques-Guillaume Legrand, with that sober pertinence which is the mark of eighteenth-century intellectuals, 'the accurate projection of his shadows and their transparency, or the fortunate liberties taken in his regard, the very indication of shadings of color are due to the

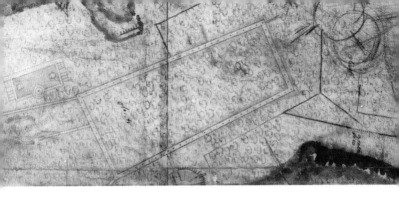

exact observation which he was to make from nature, either under the burning sun or by moonlight.' It is easy to imagine, beneath the unendurable noonday sun or at an almost luminous midnight, this observer on the prowl for the ineffable, seeking in this apparent immobility whatever moves and changes, scrutinizing ruins to discover the secret of a highlight, the place for a crosshatching, as others were to do in order to dig up treasures or to raise ghosts."

The Dark Brain of Piranesi and Other Essays,
"The Dark Brain of Piranesi", p. 93

The largest complex of the Villa's cryptoporticuses is called the Great Trapezium which is situated in the private area not open to the public, near the Odeon or Latin Theatre.
Some, among whom Falsitta, have associated such places with the underground spaces of the ritual processions, of the initiation rites, which used to take place in Eleusis and in which the Emperor had participated.

"Humanity, rightly or not, has almost always conceived of its god in terms of Providence; my duties forced me to serve as the incarnation of this Providence for one part of mankind. The more the State increases in size and power, extending its strict, cold links from man to man, the more does human faith aspire to exalt the image of a human protector at the end of this mighty chain. Whether I wished it or not, the Eastern populations of the empire already considered me a god. Even in the West, and even in Rome, where we are not officially declared divine till after death, the instinctive piety of the common people tends more and more to deify us while we are still alive. The Parthians, in gratitude to the Roman who had established and maintained peace, were soon to erect temples in my honor; even at Vologasia, in the very heart of that vast world beyond our frontiers, I had my sanctuary. Far from reading in this adoration a risk of arrogant presumption, or madness, for the man who accepts it, I found therein a restraint, and indeed an obligation to model myself upon something eternal, trying to add to my human capacity some part of supreme wisdom. To be god demands more virtues, all things considered, than to be emperor.

I was initiated at Eleusis eighteen months later. In one sense this visit to Osroës had been a turning point in my life. Instead of going back to Rome I had decided to devote some years to the Greek and Oriental prov-

inces of the empire; Athens was coming more and more to be the center of my thought, and my home. I wished to please the Greeks, and also to Hellenize myself as much as possible, but though my motives for this initiation were in part political, it proved nevertheless to be a religious experience without equal. **These ancient rites serve only to symbolize what happens in human life, but the symbol has a deeper purport than the act, explaining each of our motions in terms of celestial mechanism.** What is taught at Eleusis must remain secret; it has, besides, the less danger of being divulged in that its nature is ineffable. If formulated, it would result only in common places; therein lies its real profundity. The higher degrees which were later

conferred upon me in the course of private talks with the Hierophant added almost nothing to that first emotion which I shared in common with the least of the pilgrims who made the same ritual ablutions and drank at the spring. I had heard the discords resolving into harmonies; for one moment I had stood on another sphere and contemplated from afar, but also from close by, that procession which is both human and divine, wherein I, too, had my place, this our world where suffering existed still, but error was no more. From such a perspective **our human destiny**, that vague design in which the least practiced eye can trace so many flaws, **gleamed bright like the patterns of the heavens."**

Memoirs of Hadrian, pp. 145-146

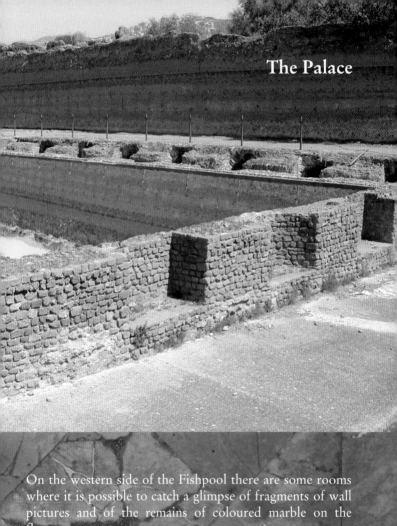

The Palace

On the western side of the Fishpool there are some rooms where it is possible to catch a glimpse of fragments of wall pictures and of the remains of coloured marble on the floors.

A small passageway, with a square opening in the ceiling, gives us the opportunity to see clearly how knowledge of the stars, and familiarity with the sky at different hours during the different seasons, may help us to know which stars are in the sky even in the daytime. Even when the light of the sun does not permit us to the see the stars, the entire celestial vault continues its rotation, which we can observe during the period of darkness. The latitude of the observation post and the hour and date of observation determine the part of the celestial sphere that is above the horizon. A portable map of the sky is a simple paper instrument that can be useful to anyone who wishes to know which constellations can be seen at a given hour of a given day of the year.

"I know exactly, at the hour of this writing, what stars are passing here at Tibur above this stuccoed and painted ceiling; and elsewhere, far away, over a tomb. Some years later it was death which was to become the object of my constant contemplation, the thought to which I was to give every faculty of my mind not absorbed by the State. And who speaks of death speaks also of that mysterious world to which, perhaps, we gain access by death. After such long reflection, and so many experiments, some of them reprehensible, I still know nothing of what goes on behind death's dark curtain. But the Syrian night [spent entirely in the contemplation of the stars (ed.)] remains as my conscious experience of immortality."

Memoirs of Hadrian, p. 149

"In my wakeful hours I took to pacing the corridors of the Villa, proceeding from room to room, sometimes disturbing a mason at work as he laid a mosaic. I would examine, in passing, a Satyr of Praxiteles and then would pause before the effigies of the beloved dead. Each room had its own, and each portico. Sheltering the flame of my lamp with my hand, I would lightly touch that breast of stone."

Memoirs of Hadrian, p. 229

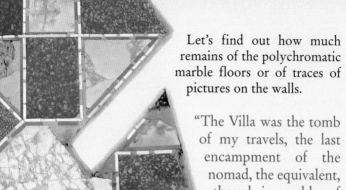

Let's find out how much remains of the polychromatic marble floors or of traces of pictures on the walls.

"The Villa was the tomb of my travels, the last encampment of the nomad, the equivalent, though in marble, of the tents and pavilions of the princes of Asia. Almost everything that appeals to our taste has already been tried in the world of forms; I turned toward the realm of color: jasper as green as the depths of the sea, porphyry dense as flesh, basalt and somber obsidian. The crimson of the hangings was adorned with more and more intricate embroideries; the mosaics of the walls or pavements were never too golden, too white, or too dark. Each building-stone was the strange concretion of a will, a memory, and sometimes a challenge. Each structure was the chart of a dream."

Memoirs of Hadrian, pp. 128

The Stadium

Looking towards the west from the Palace, we see, below, a garden called the Stadium. This space, known as the Stadium, was perhaps meant for a different purpose. However, either here, or standing before the scale model of a stadium built in marble, found between the Large Baths and the Canopus, we can read some thoughts on sport, training, and the body.

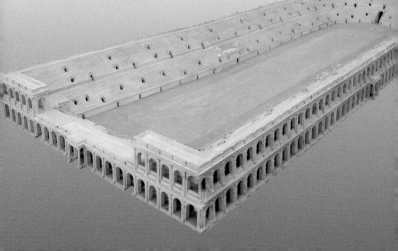

"Running, even for the shortest distance, would today be as impossible for me as for a heavy statue, a Caesar of stone; but I recall my childhood races on the dry hills of Spain, and the game played with myself of pressing on to the last gasp, never doubting that the perfect heart and healthy lungs would re-establish their equilibrium; and with any athlete training for the stadium I have a common understanding which the intelligence alone would not have given me. Thus from each art practiced in its time I derive a knowledge which compensates me in part for pleasures lost. I have supposed, and in my better moments think so still, that it would be possible in this manner to participate in the existence of everyone; such sympathy would be one of the least revocable kinds of immortality. There have been moments when that comprehension tried to go beyond human experience, passing from the swimmer to the wave. But in such a realm, since there is nothing exact left to guide me, I verge upon the world of dream and metamorphosis."

Memoirs of Hadrian, pp. 7-8

The west and the tomb on the bank of the Tiber on the horizon

"Also he constructed [...] a tomb on the bank of the Tiber."

Spartianus, XIX

On clear days, and when not blinded by the light of the setting sun it is possible to see clearly, towards the horizon in the west, Saint Peter's Cupola. Next to the cupola there is Castel Sant'Angelo, built on the Mausoleum that Hadrian had built in the city for himself, for his loved ones, and for the emperors who were to follow him.

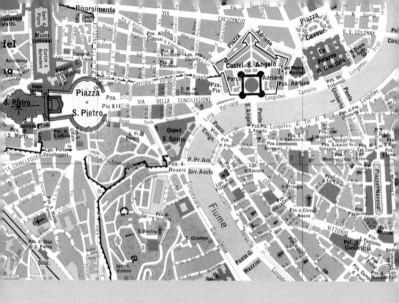

"The massive reef in the distance, perceptible in the dark, that gigantic base of my tomb so newly begun on the banks of the Tiber, suggested to me no regret at the moment, no terror nor vain meditation upon the brevity of life."

Memoirs of Hadrian, p. 171

"In Rome they were enlarging my mausoleum, since Decrianus had cleverly redrawn the plans; they are still at work upon it, even now. The idea for those circular galleries came from Egypt, and likewise the ramps descending to underground chambers; I had

conceived of a colossal tomb to be reserved not for myself alone, or for my immediate successors, but as the eventual resting-place of future emperors for centuries to come."

Memoirs of Hadrian, p. 227

"My tomb on the bank of the Tiber reproduces, on a gigantic scale, the ancient vaults of the Appian Way, but its very proportions transform it, recalling Ctesiphon and Babylon with their terraces and towers by which man seeks to climb nearer the stars."

Memoirs of Hadrian, p. 128

To the Piazza d'Oro: the east, dawn, the mountain

The Piazza d'Oro (Golden Square) is the most easterly part of the Villa. The sun rises on the facing hills. On Sant'Angelo's Hill at Arcese, at a height of circa 600 metres, there is the temple of the Bona Dea (Good Goddess), of which only a few foundation stones, hidden by brambles, now remain. Just as the west is where the sun sets, so the east is where the stars rise.

"Afterwards he sailed to Sicily, and there he climbed Mount Ætna to see the sunrise, which is many-hued, they say, like a rainbow."

Spartianus, XIII

"As he was sacrificing on Mount Casius, which he had ascended by night in order to see the sunrise, a storm arose, and a flash of lightning descended and struck both the victim and the attendant."

Spartianus, XIV

"They had told me much of the curious colors of dawn on the Ionian Sea, when beheld from the heights of Ætna. I decided to make the ascent of the mountain. We passed from the region of vines to the beds of lava, and on to the snow; the agile youth fairly ran on those steep slopes, but the scientists who went with me climbed by muleback. At the summit a shelter had been built for us to **await the dawn**. It came; an immense rainbow arched from horizon to horizon; on the icy crest strange fires blazed; earth and

sea spread out to view as far as Africa, within sight, and as Greece, which we merely guessed at. That was truly an Olympian height in my life. All was there, the golden fringe of cloud, the eagles, and the cupbearer of immortality."

Memoirs of Hadrian, p. 163

"A few days before the departure from Antioch I went to offer sacrifice, as in other years, on the summit of Mount Casius. The ascent was made by night; just as for Aetna, I took with me only a small number of friends used to climbing. My purpose was not simply to accomplish a propitiatory rite in that very sacred sanctuary; I wished to see from its height the phenomenon of dawn, that daily miracle which I never have contemplated without some secret cry of joy. At the topmost point the sun brightens the copper ornaments of the temple and the faces smile in full light while Asia's plains and the sea are still plunged in darkness; for the briefest moment the man who prays on that peak is sole beneficiary of the morning."

Memoirs of Hadrian, pp. 182-183

"Also he constructed [...] the temple of the Bona Dea."

Spartianus, XIX

"　　　　1 May
... For the moment the Good Goddess is my theme.
There's a natural height that gives its name to a place:
They call it The Rock: it's the bulk of the Aventine.
Remus waited there in vain, when you, the birds
Of the Palatine, granted first omens to his brother.
There the Senate founded a temple, hostile
To the sight of men, on the gently sloping ridge.
It was dedicated by an heiress of the ancient Clausi,
Who'd never given her virgin body to a man:
Livia restored it, so she could imitate her husband
And follow his lead in everything."

Ovid, *Fasti*, Book V, translation A.S. Kline

Bernini explains: "Indeed, on the calends of May a temple had also been dedicated to the Bona Dea (Good Goddess), deity of fertility and chastity. Men were not allowed in the temple. Later, however, the temple became a place for unchaste women and a site of dissoluteness."

To the male Faunus corresponds the goddess Fauna, the bountiful, the good, also known as Fatua, the prophetess, and Maia or Bona Dea, the goddess who increases the fertility of the fields and the wealth of human kind.

Ramorino, p. 225

Food

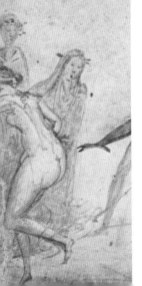

"The Piazza d'Oro was a nymphæum. This site was meant to be used for the cult of Dionysus. The nymphs, hence nymphaeum, and Dionysus symbolise the meeting of water and wine. In Rome the cult of Dionysus-Bacchus was associated with some Mystery Religion and was similar to the initiation rites of the cult of Eleusis. Hadrian participated in the cult of Dionysus throughout the Empire."

from H. Stierlin, *L'astrologia e il potere*
(*Astrology and Power*)

"...an operation which is performed two or three times a day, and the purpose of which is to sustain life, surely merits all our care. To eat a fruit is to welcome into oneself a fair living object, which is alien to us but is nourished and protected like us by the earth; it is to consume a sacrifice wherein we sustain ourselves at the expense of things. I have never bitten into a chunk of army bread without marveling that this coarse and heavy concoction can transform itself into blood and warmth, and perhaps into courage. Alas, why does my mind, even in its best days, never possess but a particle of the assimilative powers of the body? [...]

Wine initiates us into the volcanic mysteries of the soil, and its hidden mineral riches; a cup of Samos drunk at noon in the heat of the sun or, on the contrary, absorbed of a winter evening when fatigue makes the

warm current be felt at once in the hollow of the diaphragm and the sure and burning dispersion spreads along our arteries, such a drink provides a sensation which is almost sacred, and is sometimes too strong for the human head. [...]

Water drunk more reverently still, from the hands or from the spring itself, diffuses within us the most secret salt of earth and the rain of heaven.

But at certain times of life, for example in periods of ritual fasting or in the course of religious initiations, I have learned the advantage for the mind (and also the dangers) of different forms of abstinence, or even of voluntary starvation, those states approaching giddiness where the body, partly lightened of ballast, enters into a world for which it is not made."

Memoirs of Hadrian, pp. 8-11

Tempe

From Piazza d'Oro we can see westward the valley, known as Vale of Tempe, where the small Acqua Ferrata river flows. Tempe is the name of the wood on the slopes of the imposing Mount Olympus in Greece.

"Planes in space overlap likewise: Egypt and the Vale of Tempe are near, indeed, nor am I always in Tibur when I am here. Sometimes my life seems to me so commonplace as to be unworthy even of careful contemplation, let alone writing about it, and is not at all more important, even in my own eyes, than the life of any other person. Sometimes it seems to me unique, and for that very reason of no value, and useless, because it cannot be reduced to the common experience of men. No one thing explains me: neither my vices nor my

virtues serve for answer; my good fortune tells more, but only at intervals, without continuity, and above all, without logical reason. Still, the mind of man is reluctant to consider itself as the product of chance, or the passing result of destinies over which no god presides, least of all himself. A part of every life, even a life meriting very little regard, is spent in searching out the reasons for its existence, its starting point, and its source. My own failure to discover these things has sometimes inclined me toward magical explanations, and has led me to seek in the frenzies of the occult for what common sense has not taught me. When all the involved calculations prove false, and the philosophers themselves have nothing more to tell us, it is excusable to turn to the random twitter of birds, or toward the distant mechanism of the stars."

Memoirs of Hadrian, p. 26

To the Hall with Doric Pillars

We now walk back towards the Palace. We turn north and cross a space called Hall with Doric Pillars where we reflect on the "beauty" of cities.

"I felt responsible for sustaining and increasing the beauty of the world. I wanted the cities to be splendid, spacious and airy, their streets sprayed with clean water, their inhabitants all human beings whose bodies were neither degraded by marks of misery and servitude nor bloated by vulgar riches; I desired that the schoolboys should recite correctly some useful lessons; that the women presiding in their households should move with maternal dignity, expressing both vigor and calm; that the gymnasiums should be used by youths not unversed in arts and in sports; that the orchards should bear the finest fruits and the fields the richest harvests. **I desired that the might and majesty of the Roman**

Peace should extend to all, insensibly present like the music of the revolving skies; that the most humble traveller might wander from one country, or one continent, to another without vexatious formalities, and without danger, assured everywhere of a minimum of legal protection and culture; that our soldiers should continue their eternal pyrrhic dance on the frontiers; that everything should go smoothly, whether workshops or temples; that the sea should be furrowed by brave ships, and the roads resounding to frequent carriages; that, in a world well ordered, the philosophers should have their place, and the dancers also. This ideal, modest on the whole, would be often enough approached if men would devote to it one part of the energy which they expend on stupid or cruel activities; great good fortune has allowed me a partial realization of my aims during

the last quarter of a century. Arrian of Nicomedia, one of the best minds of our time, likes to recall to me the beautiful lines of ancient Terpander, defining in three words the Spartan ideal (that perfect mode of life to which Lacedaemon aspired without ever attaining it): *Strength*, *Justice*, the *Muses*. Strength was the basis, discipline without which there is no beauty, and firmness without which there is no justice. Justice was the balance of the parts, that whole so harmoniously composed which no excess should be permitted to endanger. Strength and Justice together were but one instrument, well tuned, in the hands of the Muses. All forms of dire poverty and brutality were things to forbid as insults to the fair body of mankind, **every injustice a false note to avoid in the harmony of the spheres.**"

Memoirs of Hadrian, pp. 133-135

The Hospitalia

Walking towards the north-east we reach the rooms traditionally called "Hospitalia".

Here we should turn our attention to the floor designs, mosaics in white and black tesseræ. Each room has a design in the central square area and in the three rectangular areas that open like niches on the three opposite sides of the room. The designs are based on symmetries, transfers and rotations of a module, or on the enlargement of a central motif.

At first, these mosaics made me think of the properties of figures and of theories of geometry. Later I agreed with the theory advanced by R. Pierantoni in his *Monologo sulle Stelle* (Discours on the Stars) according to which the ancient designs of mosaic floors decorations originated in the representations of the stars and the Sun, with reference to a precise understanding of light.

"...I was still more deeply absorbed in celestial mathematics, the abstract speculations to which those flaming spheres give rise... At other times I was haunted in my nightly vigils by the problem of precession of the equinoxes, as calculated long ago by Hipparchus of Alexandria. I could see in this passage and return the mathematical demonstration of those same mysteries which Eleusis represents in mere fable and symbol. In our times the Spike of Virgo is no longer at the point of the map where Hipparchus marked it, but such varia-

tion itself completes a cycle, and serves to confirm the astronomer's hypotheses. Slowly, ineluctably, this firmament will become again what it was in Hipparchus' time; it will be again what it is in the time of Hadrian. Disorder is absorbed in order, and change becomes part of a plan which the astronomer can know in advance; **thus the human mind reveals its participation in the universe by formulating such exact theorems about it, just as it does at Eleusis, by ritual outcry and dance."**

Memoirs of Hadrian, pp. 147

Sleep

In the guests' rooms we are reminded of space and of the time for rest and sleep.

"Sleep, in so short a time, had repaired my excesses of virtue with the same impartiality which it would have applied to the repair of my vices. For the divinity of the great restorer consists in bestowing his benefits upon the sleeper without concern for him, exactly as water charged with curative powers cares not at all who may drink from its source.

But if we think so little about a phenomenon which absorbs at least a third of every life it is because a certain modesty is needed to appreciate its gifts. Asleep, Caius Caligula and Aristides the Just are alike; my important but empty privileges are forgotten, and nothing distinguishes me from the black porter who lies guard at my door. What is our insomnia but the mad obstinacy of our mind in manufacturing thoughts and trains of reasoning, syllogisms and definitions of its own, refusing to abdicate in favor of that divine stupidity of closed eyes, or the wise folly of dreams? The man who cannot sleep, and I have had only too many occasions for some months to establish the point for myself, refuses more or less consciously to entrust himself to the flow of things. Brother of Death... Isocrates was wrong, and his sentence is a mere exercise in rhetoric. I begin to have some acquaintance with death; it has other secrets, more alien still to our present condition as men. And nevertheless, so intricate and so profound are these mysteries of absence and partial oblivion that we feel half assured that somewhere the white spring of sleep flows into the dark spring of death. I have never cared to gaze, as they slept, upon those I loved; they were resting from me, I know; they were escaping me, too. And every man feels some shame of his visage in the sully of sleep; how often, when I have risen early to read or to study, have I replaced the rumpled pillows myself, and the disordered covers, those almost obscene evidences of our encounters with nothingness, proofs that each night we have already ceased to be."

Memoirs of Hadrian, pp. 19-20

To the Courtyard of the Libraries

Hadrian was a frequent visitor of the Library and Museum of Alexandria: seat of learning in the arts and the sciences where books written in various languages were kept. Public libraries were not at all rare in Hellenistic cities. There were many in Rome, both private and public, the largest and most famous of which was founded by Augustus on the Palatine Hill inside the large temple of Apollo (see Pesando).

Hadrian's private library undoubtedly contained volumes and scrolls written at least in Greek and in Latin.

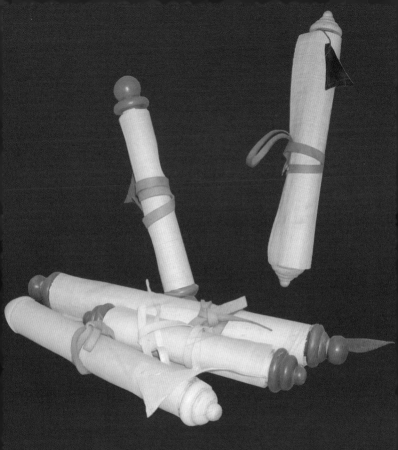

"The Villa was near enough completion to have my collections transported to it, my musical instruments and the several thousand books purchased here and there in the course of my travels."

Memoirs of Hadrian, p. 228

"A new project long occupied me, and has not ceased to do so, namely, the construction of the Odeon, a model library provided with halls for courses and lectures to serve as a center of Greek culture in Rome. I made it less splendid than the new library at Ephesus, built three or four years before, and gave it less grace and elegance than the library of Athens, but I intend to make this foundation a close second to, if not the equal of, the Museum of Alexandria; its further development will rest with you. In working upon it I often think of the library established by Plotina in Trajan's Forum, with that noble inscription placed by her order over its door: **Dispensary to the Soul**."

Memoirs of Hadrian, pp. 227-228

"Their house was only a few steps from the new library with which I had just endowed Athens, and which offered every aid to meditation, or to the repose which must precede it: comfortable chairs and adequate heating for winters which are often so sharp; stairways giving ready access to the galleries where books are kept; a luxury of alabaster and gold, quiet and subdued. Particular attention had been paid to the choice of lamps, and to their placing. I felt more and more the need to gather together and conserve our ancient books, and to entrust the making of new copies to conscientious scribes. This noble task seemed to me no

less urgent than aid to veterans or sub-
sidies to prolific families of the poor;
I warned myself that it would take
only a few wars, and the misery that
follows them, or a single period of
brutality or savagery under a few
bad rulers to destroy forever
the ideas passed down with
the help of these frail
objects in fiber
and ink. Each
man fortu-
nate enough
to benefit to
some degree from
this legacy of cul-
ture seemed to
me responsible for
protecting it and
holding it in trust
for the human
race."

Memoirs of Hadrian,
pp. 216-217

"Anyone who loves
life loves not only
the present but also

the past, for the simple reason that the past, as I can't remember which Greek poet once said, outweighs the present, especially the narrow individual present that each one of us knows. Thus it is only natural for a person who truly loves life to read a great deal. [...]
After a while I had reconstructed for myself Hadrian's cultural universe: I knew more or less what he read, what his points of reference were [...]"

"The great men of the past [...] are our role models and guides, but it would not be right if the dissatisfaction we feel with so many aspects of the modern world should now turn us into idolaters of the past. Today's evil as well as good, has its roots in yesteryear. Of the great men [...] most had their faults, and they all witnessed scenes almost as dreadful as those before our own eyes. Cicero was sometimes a devious politician. He lived during the most brilliant, but also in the most brutal and politically corrupt years of the end of the Republic, before dying a victim of Octavian's dreadful proscription; Marcus Aurelius was one of the most noble souls ever to have lived on Earth, but his wise and profound disillusionment often became a kind of dismal apathy; his religious acceptance of the order of things sometimes made him see the mistakes of his time as inevitable or necessary (as we do, with the mistakes of our time); his weakness with regard to natural affections (his wife, his son, his adoptive brother) led him into error and abuse from which he so admirably struggled to escape; he was responsible for the worst persecution of Christian minorities; he initiated fewer useful reforms than emperors less wise than he; and the relatively calm world in which he lived was destined soon to face a darker future. […] It is the same for literature in its proper sense; the great works of the past are surely greatly superior to the poor offerings of today, but that is due in part to the fact that we only see the best works of the past, because the mediocre works have fallen into oblivion. Indeed, we cannot carefully gather up all the great thoughts and role models of the past to teach and to guide us, and to guard us against the prejudices of our time, and against ourselves, but let us not count on definitive models and reliable guides. It is up to us to try in our own way to be as good, or a little better."

Lettres à ses amis et quelques autres, Petite Plaisance, January 1963, pp. 180-181

"Thus, since one of the best ways to reconstruct a man's thinking is to rebuild his library, I had actually been working for years, without knowing it, to refurnish the bookshelves at Tibur in advance. Now I had only to imagine the swollen hands of a sick man holding the half-rolled manuscripts."

Reflections on the Composition of Memoirs of Hadrian, p. 325

The Maritime Theatre

From the library courtyard, by means of a small staircase situated under the Tower, we reach the circular corridor inside the Maritime Theatre.
We have reached the heart of the Villa, a place that owing to its shape is especially inviting. Here we marvel at the reflections of the sky and of the sunlight on the water and on the stones, and at the reflections of the moon or of the clouds on the water.

"I have tried under many a form to join the divine, and have known more than one ecstasy; some of these have been atrocious, others overpoweringly sweet, but the one of the Syrian night [spent entirely in the observation of the constellations (ed.)] was strangely lucid. It inscribed within me the heavenly motions with greater precision than any partial observation would ever have allowed me to attain."

Memoirs of Hadrian, p. 149

"Everything here was arranged to facilitate work as well as pleasure: the chancellery, the audience halls, and the court where I judged difficult cases in last appeal all saved me the tiring journeys between Tibur and Rome. **I had given each of these edifices names reminiscent of Greece: the Pœcile, the Academy, the Prytaneum**. I knew very well that this small valley planted with olive trees was not Tempe, but I was reaching the age when each beauteous place recalls another, fairer still, when each delight is weighted with the memory of past joys. I was willing to yield to nostalgia, that melancholy residue of desire. I had even given the name of Styx to a particularly somber corner of the park, and the name of Elysian Fields to a meadow strewn with anemones, thus preparing myself for that other world where the torments resemble those of this world, but where joys are nebulous, and inferior to our joys. But

most important of all, in the heart of this retreat I had
built for myself a refuge more private still, an islet of
marble at the center of a pool surrounded by colonnades; this gave me a room wholly apart, connected
with, or rather, separated from the shore by a turning
bridge so light that with one hand I could make it slide
in its grooves. Into this summer pavilion I had two
or three beloved statues moved, and the small bust of
Augustus as a child, which Suetonius had given me
in the period when we still were friends; I used to go
there at the hour of siesta to sleep or to think, or to
read. My dog would stretch out across the doorway,
extending his paws somewhat stiffly now; reflections
played on the marble; Diotimus would rest his cheek,
to cool himself, against the smooth surface of an urn;
my thoughts were on my successor."

Memoirs of Hadrian, p. 252-253

"My frequest sojourns in Asia Minor had put me in touch with a small group of scholars seriously concerned with the study of magic arts. Each century has its particular daring: the boldest minds of our time, weary of a philosophy which grows more and more academic, are venturing to explore those frontiers forbidden to mankind. In Tyre, Philo of Byblus had revealed to me certain secrets of ancient Phoenician magic; he continued in my suite to Antioch. There Numenius was giving a new interpretation to Plato's myths on the nature of the soul; his theories remained somewhat timid, but they would have led far a hardier intelligence than his own. His disciples could summon spirits; for us that was

a game like many another. Strange faces which seemed made of the very marrow of my dreams appeared to me in the smoke of the incense, then wavered and dissolved, leaving me only the feeling that they resembled some known, living visage. All that was no more, perhaps, than a mere juggler's trick, but in this case the juggler knew his trade.

I went back to the study of anatomy, barely approached in my youth, but now it was no longer a question of sober consideration of the body's structure. I was seized with curiosity to investigate those intermediate regions where the soul and the flesh intermingle, where dream echoes reality, or sometimes even precedes it, where life and death exchange attributes and masks. My physician Hermogenes disapproved of such experiments, but nevertheless he acquainted me with a few practitioners who worked along these lines. I tried with them to find the exact seat of the soul and the bonds which attach it to the body, and to measure the time which it takes to detach itself. Some animals were sacrificed to this research. The surgeon Satyr us took me into his hospital to witness death agonies. We speculated together: is the soul only the supreme development of the body, the fragile evidence of the pain and pleasure of existing? Is it, on the contrary, more ancient than the body, which is modeled on its image and which serves it momentarily, more or less well, as instrument? Can it be called back inside the flesh, re-establishing with the body that close union and mutual combustion which we name life? If souls possess an identity of their own, can they be interchanged, going from one being to another like a segment of fruit or the sip of wine which two lovers exchange in a kiss? Every philosopher changes his opinion about these things some twenty times a year; in my case skepticism contended with desire to know, and enthusiasm with irony. But I felt convinced that our brain allows only the merest residue of facts to filter through to us: I began to be more and more interested in the obscure world of sensation, dark as night, but where blinding suns mysteriously flash and revolve."

Memoirs of Hadrian, pp. 180-182

"As in the days of my felicity, people believe me to be a god; they continue to give me that appellation even though they are offering sacrifices to the heavens for the restoration of the Imperial Health. I have already told you the reasons for which such a belief, salutary for them, seems to me not absurd. A blind old woman has come on foot from Pannonia, having undertaken that exhausting journey in order to ask me to touch her eyes; she has recovered her sight under my hands, as her fervor had led her to expect; her faith in the emperor-god explains this miracle. Other prodigies have occurred, and invalids say that they have seen me in their dreams, as the pilgrims to Epidaurus have visions of Æsculapius; they claim that they have awakened cured, or at least improved. I do not smile at the contrast between my powers as a thaumaturge and my own illness; I accept these new privileges with gravity. The old blind woman who made her way to the emperor from the depths of a barbarian province has become for me what the slave of Tarragona had formerly been, namely, a symbol of the populations of the empire whom I have both ruled and served. Their immense confidence repays me for twenty years of work which was itself congenial to me.

Phlegon has recently read me verses of a Jew of Alexandria who also attributes to me superhuman powers; without irony I welcomed that description of an elderly prince who is seen going back and forth over all the roads of the earth, descending to the treasures of the mines, reawakening the generative forces of the soil, and everywhere establishing peace and prosperity; the initiate who has restored the shrines of all races, the connoisseur in magic arts, the seer who raised a youth to the heavens. I shall have been better understood by this enthusiastic Jew than by many a senator and proconsul; this adversary now won over looks upon me almost as does Arrian; I am amazed to have become for people just what I sought to be, after all, and I marvel that this success is made up of so little.

Old age and death, as they approach, begin to add their majesty to this prestige; men step reverently from my path; they no longer compare me, as they once did, to serene and radiant Zeus, but to Mars Gradivus, god of long campaigns and austere discipline, or to grave Numa, inspired by the gods. Of late this pale, drawn visage, these fixed eyes and this tall body held straight by force of will, suggest to them Pluto, god of shades."

Memoirs of Hadrian, pp. 284-286

"*G:* With the difference that Hadrian, as emperor, was by Roman law also a god.
Y: He was one of the first to enjoy the position of divine emperor, because the practice of apotheosizing the emperor during his lifetime, which originated in the East, was not adopted in Rome until Hadrian's time

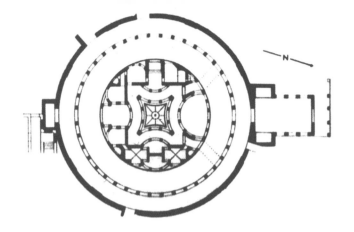

or shortly thereafter. Augustus was not apotheosized until after his death. It is true, however, that Hadrian did, toward the end of his life, begin to arouse religious enthusiasm. One sees this quite clearly in contemporary documents. People believed in a form of power, or charisma, to use modern theological jargon."

With Open Eyes, p. 123

"The Maritime Theatre is also called the Theatre of the Universe, The Royal Hall for the worship of the Emperor, the island of Earthly Paradise. There were plants grouped so as to form a thicket, fish in the water, and sparrows in the sky. There were elements of trabeation above the fluted columns, with friezes adorned with sea monsters, tritons, nereids, chariots driven by various animals, and birds led by genii."

notes from *Villa Adriana* by Aurigemma

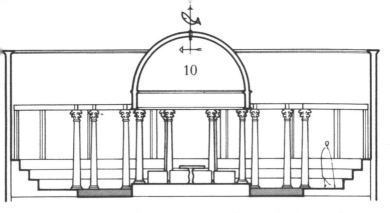

"The astro-meteorology, as seen in the mechanism of the Aviary of Varrone, with its vane attached to a planetarium showing the time, is based on the idea that there is a connexion between the meteorological phenomena and the planets. Ptolemy, a contemporary of Hadrian, pursuing this idea, connects to each of the 4 main winds, a group of 3 signs of the Zodiac. The winds are placed on the same level as the universal breath, through which the link between Earth and the stars is established.

The central island of the circular space represents Earth, surrounded by water, the primordial Ocean, the river of time with its cyclical returns in an infinite motion.

With its concentric circles, this structure is the image of the celestial mechanism, "imago mundi", and of the cosmos.

The power that the emperor has on time, a power that he exercises through astrology and the administration of justice, grants him the right to be worshipped as a god.

Perhaps, in the Maritime Theatre there was something similar to the Aviary of Varrone."

from Henri Stierlin, *L'Astrologia e il potere* (*Astrology and Power*)

Towards the exit

"Evening approaches, as golden as the morning and the height of the day have been. The tree tops close in, accepting the evening with the same grace with which they accepted the dawn. A little light lingers at the bottom of the valley like a small amount of water collected in the palm of a cool hand. Night hovers, woven with gold, like a divine cloth. Darkness here is more motherly, more brotherly than loving: the Great Mother becomes a Good Virgin. Demeter becomes Persephone again; Latona becomes Artemis again. Slowly Earth's lap is covered with starry velvet. Hera's milk, gushing from a bite in her blue breast, flows in the Milky Way. The shadow where all becomes Shadow, in the palaestra, barely enables one to recognise the slenderest of columns, now a solitary stem, around which the

young contestants would put their arms, as if around a waist, and at which one cannot look without thinking of Hippolytus. Life, passionate cruel mother, rejected in the form of Phaedra, called forth a monster that Hercules would easily defeat, but whose mere breath was enough to destroy this young innocent, this young flower. Then Death fatal, reassuring, lunar, came to him in the form of Artemis. He sensed her presence without seeing her, because the dying can only sense the gods. And we who unceasingly move towards our death, we, too, have been unable to see Artemis. But here we breathe in her fragrance of grass and stars, and lying under this sky, under these fires, we hold on to the night as though it were the hem of her mantle."

1934 (1970) – *En pèlerin et en étranger*, p. 13

"They're really methods of contemplation. It is true that, in writing *Hadrian*, I occasionally made use of various contemplative methods. I still use them, moreover. Some of them I've worked out for myself, while others came from my study of oriental philosophy, among other things."

With Open Eyes, p. 118

"What matters is the full realization of a man's destiny as statesman – and also, in the end, as a human being, for though few people know it, every human life is fundamentally divine."

With Open Eyes, p. 123

"I had written the story of a man who was both a prince and a supremely interesting individual, and for some reason it met with great success. It is always pleasant to give a figure from the past a new lease on life."

With Open Eyes, p. 129

Chronology

76   Hadrian born at Italica (Spain) 24 January

117   Hadrian becomes Emperor

121   Hadrian journeys to Egypt

130   Hadrian travels in Egypt, death of Antinous

137   The constellation of Antinous is added to the Almagest by Ptolemy (Alexandria of Egypt)

138   Hadrian dies at Baiae 10 July

Bibliography

Dion Cassius, *Histoire Romaine*, LXVI vol. 9, St. Genevieve library, Paris, volume 69 on Hadrian, pp. 460-509 (Greek and French texts)

Ælius Spartianus, *The Life of Hadrian*
"The Internet History Sourcebook"
www.fordham.edu/halsall

Ovid, *Fasti*, translation by A.S. Kline
Ovid, *The Metamorphoses*, translation by A.S. Kline
"Poetry In Translation" – www.tonykline.co.uk

S. Aurigemma, *Villa Adriana*, Istituto poligrafico e Zecca dello Stato, Rome 1984

F. Ramorino, *Mitologia classica illustrata*, Hoepli, Milan 1984

F. Gregorovius, *Vita di Adriano*, Fratelli Melita Editori, La Spezia 1988 (I ed 1910)

H. Stierlin, *Hadrien et l'architecture romaine*, Office du Livre, Fribourg (Switzerland) 1984

H. Stierlin, *Inde. Des Moghols aux Maharajas*, Editions Payot, Paris 1985

H. Stierlin, *L'astrologie et le pouvoir. De Platon à Newton*, Paris 1986

F. Pesando, *Libri e biblioteche*, Edizioni Quasar, Rome 1994

M. Falsitta, *Villa Adriana – una questione di composizione architettonica*, Skira, Milan 2000

R. Pierantoni, *Monologo sulle stelle*, Bollati Boringhieri, Turin 1994

W. MacDonald, J.A. Pinto, *Villa Adriana – la costruzione e il mito da Adriano a Louis Kahn*, Electa, Milan 1997

AA.VV., *Hadrien empereur et architecte*, Vögele Edition, Genève 2002

Villa Adriana – paesaggio antico e ambiente moderno, M. Reggiani (Ed.), Electa, Milan 2002

Illustrations

Notes

Notes

Notes

Contents

Photography authorized by the Soprintendenza per i Beni
Archeologici del Lazio.

Original title: *Villa Adriana tra cielo e terra. Percorsi guidati dai
testi di Marguerite Yourcenar*, by Nicoletta Lanciano.
Apeiron Editori, Sant'Oreste (Rome), 2003

Translation: Amina Santcross

Design and lay-out: Maria Korporal
www.mariakorporal.com

Printed by Union Printing S.p.a.
S.S. Cassia Nord, km 87
01100 Viterbo – Italy

ISBN 88-85978-31-2

First edition, Sant'Oreste (Roma), 2005

© Apeiron Editori S.n.c.
Località Pantano
00060 Sant'Oreste RM – Italy

www.apeironbookservice.com